With best wishes
from
Maureen Melvin
and

Abigail

PAWS FOREVER

MAUREEN MELVIN
Illustrated by Geoff Crook

CHAPMANS

Also by Maureen Melvin
with illustrations by Geoff Crook

PAWS FOR THOUGHT
PAWS AGAIN
PAWS FOR PASTA

For countless evenings spent *à deux*
And walks along the shore,
And happy days remembered here
In Paws Forevermore.

Chapmans Publishers
A division of the Orion Publishing Group Ltd
Orion House
5 Upper St Martin's Lane
London WC2H 9EA

A CIP catalogue record for this book is available from the British Library

ISBN 1 85592 682 2

First published by Chapmans 1993

Designed by Judy Linard

Typeset by Deltatype Ltd, Ellesmere Port, Cheshire

Printed in Great Britain by
Butler and Tanner Ltd, Frome and London

Author's Note

This book, I think, will be my last;
It's time to take a rest.
I've got arthritis in my paw
And gremlins in my chest.

Old age is creeping up on me,
My hair is turning grey,
I'm deaf as the proverbial post
And slower every day.

I can't complain: I'm twelve years old
And busy as can be.
I eat a splendid gourmet lunch,
Then write each day till tea.

So don't be sad or shed a tear
Because I've had my day.
Read on, my friends and you will see
That *PAWS* are here to stay!

Paws for Charity

I plan to hold an auction for the Guy Dogs:
It's going to be a fabulous affair.
And I'm forming a committee
With some big-wigs in the city
So everyone who's someone will be there.

I'm asking all my friends if they'll support me
And bring along some treasures I can sell.
I've a First World War propeller
Which I dug up in the cellar
And a piece of Roman pottery as well.

I'll have to make some rules and regulations;
No bones allowed, unless they're really old.
I'll take coins and silver dollars
But no ornamental collars,
Except the ones with diamonds, pearls and gold.

When Mummy saw my poster for the auction
She patted me and smiled and shook her head.
'Just a small mistake,' said she,
'Look – it's Guide Dogs – with a "d".'
'I know,' I said, 'Guy Dogs – that's what I said!'

Sometimes she's unbelievably provoking.
I try to keep my cool and stay polite.
But I feel my hackles rising
For she's always criticizing
And anyhow, this time I'm sure I'm right.

You have to be well-schooled to be a Guy Dog;
Some even land a job with an MP.
They can lend their canine weight
To each pertinent debate
And linger in the Commons for their tea.

The barn will be ideal for the proceedings.
I practise with my gavel every night.
I shall be the auctioneer
And I'd like to make it clear
That prices will be soaring out of sight.

So look out for the details of my auction
And don't assume I'm sticking out my neck.
You won't think it quite so funny
When I'm raking in the money
And writing out an astronomic cheque!

Strictly for the Birds

I find, now I am older
And a little more mature,
I need fresh inspiration
To enhance my literature.

When *Paws for Thought* was published,
Well, I really had a ball.
My Author's Tour in London
Was the finest day of all.

I visited my P.R. girls
And briefed them, blow by blow,
Then went to see my publisher,
A camera man in tow.

I chose the boardroom table,
To be photographed in style,
Shook hands with all the big-wigs,
While the flash preserved my smile.

We stopped, between engagements,
In St James's Park, to rest,
And there I met a squirrel
Who was furnishing his nest.

I much admired his bushy tail,
His neat and shiny head.
He gazed at me, I gazed at him,
But not a word was said.

His eyes were speaking volumes;
And I answered him in kind.
We stood there, rooted to the spot,
Conversing – mind to mind.

He had to beat the winter,
Storing nuts in every nook.
I told him of my Author's Tour
And hoped he'd like my book.

I planned to visit him again
And fixed a likely date,
Then taxied off to Harrods
For I'm never, ever late.

I had to meet the doorman
For some photographs, *à deux*.
A poodle, who was passing by,
Cried, 'Get a load of HER!'

I grabbed a slender bite to eat,
Then dashed to catch the train.
A little snooze, then we were back
In Gloucestershire again.

So, after all the fun and games,
Life's just too dull for words.
And plodding up the lane at home
Is strictly for the birds!

In the Money

I'm opening up a bank account in person;
I'm going to have a cheque book of my own,
For I'm sick of being harassed
And financially embarrassed
When I'm shopping at the butchers for a bone.

I'm off to London town to meet my agent;
I'll choose a bank to handle my affairs.
There'll be cut-throat competition,
'Cos I'm quite an acquisition
For the moneymen and city millionaires.

Of course, I have collateral to offer –
My talent and extraordinary good looks.
Well, no banker could decline
A portfolio like mine
Or a famous canine author on his books.

Mistaken Identity

I was working on my latest book one warm September day
And the garden door was standing open wide.
I'd ignored a noisy pheasant and the drifts of new mown hay
And the woodland creatures calling me outside.

Then a shadow fell across a shaft of sunlight by the door
So I swivelled round to see what it could be.
And in solitary splendour in the middle of the floor
Was a mighty fieldmouse looking straight at me.

I wondered why he'd ventured in on such a lovely day;
I could see he was exceedingly well-built.
But the moment I approached him he was up and on his way.
And he bolted round the cloakroom door – full tilt.

I nosed around the skirting board to test the atmosphere
But my uninvited guest had gone to ground.
I retreated to my writing desk and cocked a random ear
But of mouse there was no smell or sight or sound.

There were no more interruptions till the moon was riding high
When a shady figure skimmed across the floor.
With my dream on hold, I surfaced and unzipped a sleepy eye,
As he squeezed himself beneath the kitchen door.

A Sorry Tale

When Daddy travels round the world
And comes back home to base,
There's always Something Nice for me
Tucked down inside his case.

Returning from the States last time
He really scored a hit,
Some trendy black designer boots,
I only hoped they'd fit.

He said that they were all the rage
With dogs in ol' New York.
No canine there would dare to go
Unbooted on her walk.

I'm known to be a fashion buff,
Distinctly avant-garde.
I couldn't wait to get them on
And strut around the yard.

I pulled and tugged and tugged and pulled,
My efforts were in vain.
I prised the silver buckles loose,
Then pulled and tugged again.

A tear rolled down my whiskers,
It was plain for all to see,
Those boots were made for walking
But those boots were not for me.

We took them to the Oxfam shop.
The lady liked them fine.
I hope they find a little dog
With smaller paws than mine.

Down Under

Guess what! I've had letters from dogs in Australia
And pressing entreaties to stay.
So I'll pack up my traps and I'll charter a schooner
And set out for Botany Bay.

I'll line up some Paws who are ready to crew
'Cos I'm not *au courant* with the sea.
I'll take Harry and Bumble and Mickey, the doc,
While the captain, of course, will be me.

Now Harry can shin up the ropes like a monkey
And Bumble will victual the boat.
There'll be daily inspections conducted by Mickey,
His stethoscope tucked in his coat.

Should I be unmanned as we buffet through Biscay –
A touch of the old *mal de mer* –
I can safely leave Harry in charge at the helm
While I throw up in private, elsewhere.

I see, from my map, there's an easier way
To get through to the ends of the earth,
So I'm starting at dawn with my pickaxe and spade
And I'm aiming for Brisbane or Perth.

The Christmas Present

A lovely thing happened last Christmas –
A present came out of the blue,
When the mailman called out from his van at the gate
'Hi there, Abigail, here's one for you!'

I saw that the postmark was Cheltenham,
So I checked my address book to see
Which of all my good friends might have pushed out the boat
And acquired something special for me.

There's a canine boutique based in Cheltenham:
It stocks the most elegant togs.
They sell paintings and porcelain and *PAWS* books, of course,
And the latest in fashion for dogs.

With seven days, still, before Christmas
I promised to put it away.
I secreted it under my beanbag each night
And I shook it a little each day.

I snipped it undone in a second.
Eureka! Just wait for it, girls –
Lying there was the best thing I ever had seen,
A magnificent collar of pearls.

They were strung on a flexible necklace.
I tried it for size, in a daze.
At the front was a pendant, a tiny gold bone,
En tremblant, I think that's the phrase.

In the box was a card from the owner
Of that wonderful Cheltenham boutique.
They had sold all my books and had sent me the pearls
As a pat on the back, so to speak.

I've never had such a fine present;
I'll never get over the thrill.
I shall wear it whenever I'm out on the town
And it goes to my heirs in my will.

A Classic Example

When someone has a clever wheeze
It's bound to be the Japanese.
CDs for cats and dogs – what next!
I bet Lloyd Webber's really vexed.

For, having scored a hit with *CATS*,
It's quite enough to drive him bats
To think he could have missed the boat
To get this new idea afloat.

Research has been entailed, I know,
By Japanese in Tokyo,
To set the music world agog
With Compact Discs for cat and dog.

Now, I was born to spend my days
Where every kind of music plays.
My taste is wide, though I confess
I'm very fond of G and S.

Why can't Lloyd Webber do for dogs
What he's already done for mogs?
Now, that would cut more ice with me
Than any avant-garde CD.

French with Tears

I tried to learn French for my cookery book,
Though I found it a terrible bore.
There were nouns by the dozen and verbs by the yard
And those culinary terms by the score.

Then Daddy came into the kitchen one day
With a dictionary – one of his own.
It was French into English and English to French
And he said I could have it – on loan.

It was bound in green leather, hand tooled and embossed,
And the pages were sprinkled with gold.
It was quite the most beautiful book I had seen;
It was more than a hundred years old.

Left alone with my work, I examined this tome
And it gave off a wonderful smell.
If I ate my way through it – I thought to myself –
I'd absorb *le français* really well.

I started at 'A' and I nibbled straight through
Till I came to a halt at *baguette*.
Then I stopped for a snooze, for I needed a break
To keep everything clear *dans ma tête*.

I awoke with a start to find Daddy returned,
His expression a sight to behold.
I had green on my whiskers, my chest and my paws
And my nose was all covered in gold.

Daddy's face wasn't green, it was purple with rage.
'You ungrateful young pup!' thundered he.
I'm not young or a pup but I just let it pass,
It was clearly the doghouse for me.

Well – so much for initiative, drive and pizzazz:
There's a moral involved somewhere here.
For the longest way round is the shortest way home
And I've learnt it the hard way, I fear.

Avoirdupois

They've started a Weight-Watchers Club at the vet's
And I go for the weigh-in each week.
I resent lining up with those pot-bellied pets,
After all, I'm a priceless antique!

When I step on the scales I'm the heaviest yet
And the needle swings higher each time.
It's supposed to go down, but I think they forget
I'm a lady who's well past her prime.

I've been given a list headed 'AVOIRDUPOIS',
That's my Weight-Watchers name, it's brand new.
All the things I'm allowed are, of course, my *bêtes noires*,
All the things I adore are taboo.

If I diet any more I shall ruin my looks
'Cos my lunch has already been halved.
I need masses of vigour for signing my books
And I don't want to turn up half-starved.

Driving home in the car we examine my plight
And the problem that's vexed me for years.
Mummy thinks I should cut out my biscuit at night.
I agree, though I'm nearly in tears.

In the sweet by-and-by when I'm slender and sleek
And you're summoned to dinner *chez moi*,
You'll be able to savour your Sole Véronique
With the gorgeous Miss Avoir-du-Pois.

The Wedding

You wouldn't believe the excitement
When Nick married Sarah last Spring.
I'm pleased it was Sarah, I like her a lot
And she's mad about dogs – that's the thing!

I've never heard so much discussion
About waistcoats and cufflinks and ties.
All the men in my family are frightfully smart;
Even Mummy looks nice when she tries.

It struck me, as D-Day drew nearer
While packing my present to send
That my own invitation had failed to appear
And I hadn't been asked to attend.

Then Mummy came clean and informed me:
The logistics could not be resolved.
She employs these longs words just to blind me with science
But I understood what was involved.

It meant I'd be left as a watchdog
While everyone went to the ball.
Though a friend might drop in for a spot of cold lunch,
There'd be no conversation at all.

In fact that's exactly what happened:
They left me alone, in the lurch.
But I thought of them all at a quarter to three
And imagined myself at the church.

I dreamed I was Sarah's chief bridesmaid,
Attending her all through the day.
As they left for their honeymoon, Sarah turned back
And she tossed me her lovely bouquet.

Weeks later they showed me the pictures.
There wasn't a bridesmaid my size.
But one thing had been kept as a secret till then
And it came as a splendid surprise.

The wedding cake looked quite fantastic.
I've copied it so you can see
That as part of the frieze, round the centremost tier,
Was a beautiful portrait of me.

The dog at the bottom is Rosie,
She's Sarah's black Labrador friend
You can see Nick's guitars on the cake at the top –
We were all in the act at the end.

Oh, wasn't it thoughtful of Sarah
To make me a part of her day!
And I don't feel so sad that I missed all the fun
Now I know I was there on display.

They gave us the cake as a present;
I didn't have any to try.
And it's gone in the freezer till goodness knows when
So I might as well wish it goodbye!

Up and Away!

I was checking out the garden on my daily dawn patrol,
When a movement in the flower-bed caught my eye.
And it wasn't Fred the Fieldmouse and it wasn't Mick the Mole,
But a baby blackbird learning how to fly.

He'd been taking flying lessons and he must have had a fall,
For he flapped and squawked and struggled round and round.
Mrs Blackbird scolded loudly from above the garden wall,
But he simply couldn't make it off the ground.

His mother fluttered up and down, then flew off in despair
And the only one to sort things out was me.
Then I spied a slab of paving stone beneath the Weeping Pear –
It would make a perfect launch pad, I could see.

I pushed the slab towards the bird and nudged him with my nose,
Very gently till I had him on the spot.
This entailed a sharp encounter with a Ballerina rose
But these hybrids are a temperamental lot.

The fledgling tried his little wings, puffed out his little chest.
'You can do it now,' I said, 'go on – go on!'
He rose swiftly to the Silver Birch, paused briefly for a rest,
Then he chirruped once, soared upwards and was gone.

It wasn't long before they found the rose in disarray
And, immediately, all eyes were turned on me.
But I felt no shame; I knew that rose would bloom another day
And my little friend was flying high and free.

Paws Enterprises

I've got a tiny toothbrush –
It's custom-made for me.
I brush my choppers twice each day
And sometimes after tea.

I've got some chicken toothpaste
And strawberry flavoured too,
And special canine dental floss
Which I'm supposed to chew.

'Cos now I'm getting older
My teeth don't have much clout,
And now and then a well-worn tooth
Works loose and tumbles out.

When I was just a puppy
I didn't brush at all.
There were no dental aids for dogs,
As far as I recall.

But now it's all big business:
There's money to be made.
A canine poet like me could well
Be useful in the trade.

I might design a gadget
To stimulate the jaws,
Then all my friends will keep their teeth
By courtesy of *PAWS*.

The Smallest Room

Mummy spoke to a property dealer she'd met
And he said an extraordinary thing.
He'd been looking at houses and casting his net,
To see how many deals he could swing.

It transpired, as he toured round the crannies and nooks
Of these pads, with his eagle-eyed spouse,
That, in nine out of ten, they had spotted my books
In the tiniest room in the house.

Now, I'm not taking umbrage; I'm pleased to be read
And I don't mean to grizzle and grouse.
But my books deserve better, it has to be said,
Than the tiniest room in the house.

It is safer, in my view, to spread them about
In the boudoir, the salon, the den.
If you run to the loo and the loo roll runs out
Just imagine what might happen then!

I'll suggest to my friends – and they add up to scores –
All they need is a soupçon of nous
To come up with a pleasanter place for their *PAWS*
Than the tiniest room in the house.

'Palming the Pill'

I don't like taking pills at all,
It really gets my goat,
Especially when they grab your head
And shove them down your throat.

Now Mummy thinks she has the power
To coax me when I'm ill.
She finds a tasty scrap of meat
And wraps it round the pill.

Sometimes it's in a piece of fish,
Sometimes a slice of ham.
I sit there like a statue
And I take it like a lamb.

'Good girl!' she'll say and pat my head –
I'm too choked up to speak –
I down the food, extract the pill
And store it in my cheek.

And when I'm sure she's left the room
And no one is about,
I find a dark and dusty spot
And smartly spit it out.

I'll tell you now what steps I take
To help an illness pass,
I wander down a country lane
And stuff myself with grass.

Apache – He Say . . .

I know that God created man
And all that sort of thing.
He made the sun, the moon, the stars
And taught the birds to sing.

I know He loves the underdog
And those who've gone astray.
He even spells His Name like ours
But round the other way!

Apache Indians put their trust
In different kinds of god.
Some views they hold are wonderful
And some are rather odd.

But one thing sets my heart aglow,
One thing and one thing only –
The thought that God created Man
So Dog would not be lonely.

Mon Dieu!

I've been studying French which is really confusing
Without any Francophile shocks,
Like the rubbish I heard on the Nine O'Clock News
When I strolled in to look at the box.

For a lady in France made a scandalous charge,
Madame Cresson, out strutting her stuff,
Had the nerve to observe to the nation at large,
'British males are not macho enough'!

Now I don't know what knowledge she has of the breed
But I'd like to take issue on that.
Her ideas must be based on a blue-blooded weed
Or some party political prat.

All the males in my life would resent such a slur.
Take the great British Bulldog for one.
And Prince Rupert, my friend, is *un grand amoreux*,
The supreme Casanova bar none.

I shall ask Madame Cresson, as mentioned above,
  To withdraw her expression of scorn.
If she will not retract when I throw down the glove,
  Then it has to be pistols at dawn.

Forward Planning

I've taken on two sparkling young assistants
There's Annabel, a Tricolour like me,
And young Alice – quite unique,
She's a Blenheim, full of cheek –
She's going to take some training, I can see.

Now Annabel shows great poetic feeling:
I think she may surprise us all in time.
Alice, I regret to say,
Likes the poetry of to-day:
The sort that doesn't scan, make sense or rhyme.

I've worked them hard and put them through their paces,
I've taught them almost everything I know.
And by now it's quite apparent
They've inherited my talent
And they'll follow in my footsteps when I go.

I may be off to heaven at the weekend;
I've had it in my mind for quite a while.
And I've packed three angel cakes,
In case Cerberus awakes,
And my latest book to make Saint Francis smile.

I'm really looking forward to the journey.
It's bound to be the best adventure yet.
And I'll catch a shooting star
To the other side of far,
Then I'll climb aboard Saint Peter's private jet.

The Straggler will be waiting there to greet me.
He'll keep me straight until I get my wings.
He will tell our heavenly Master
How I saved him from disaster
And lots of other complimentary things.

To say goodbye to Mummy will be dreadful;
I think I'll slip away while she's asleep.
For she may not know for certain
That it's not my final curtain
And I simply cannot bear to see her weep.

This life has been a wonderful experience.
The next one will be better still, I know.
For as soon as I can fly,
I'll be chasing round the sky
And keeping watch on everyone below.